nufonia must fall

Published by UNI Books, CP 60114 Saint-Denis, Montreal, QC H2J 4E1 Canada

LIBRARY AND ARCHIVES CANADA CATALOGUING IN PUBLICATION DATA

Kid Koala author, illustrator
Nufonia must fall / by Kid Koala. -- 2nd edition

Accompanied by a CD sound track.
Originally published: Toronto : ECW Press, 2003.
ISBN 978-0-9876784-1-6 (bound)

1. Graphic novels. I. Title.

PN6733.K5N83 2014   741.5'971   C2014-902817-2

The publication of *Nufonia Must Fall* has been generously supported by the Canada Council, the Ontario Arts Council, and the Government of Canada through the Book Publishing Industry Development Program.

Thank you to ECW Press.

Canada Council   Conseil des arts
for the Arts   du Canada

PRINTED AND BOUND IN CANADA BY MARQUIS

nufonia must fall

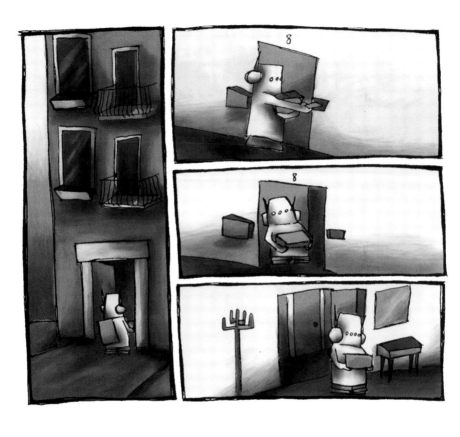

PRESENTS

nufonia must fall

story, drawings, & music by kid koala

lighting & coloring by louisa schabas

chapter 1

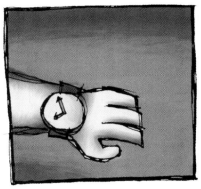

11

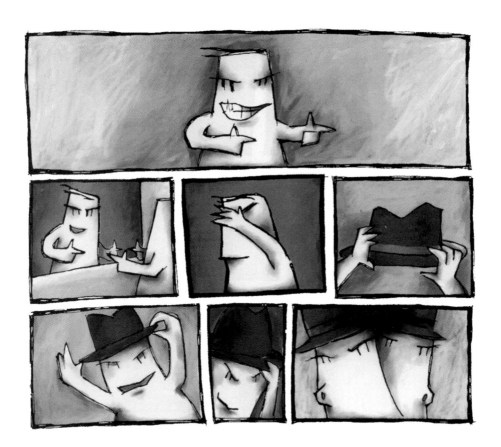

WINDSOR DRY CLEANE

SHIRTS . . . .
COATS . . . .
THONGS . . . .

TUNA
BLUEBERRY JAM
URCHIN
CARROT & RAISINS

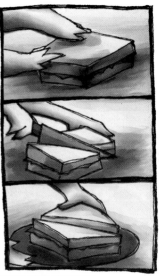

click

27

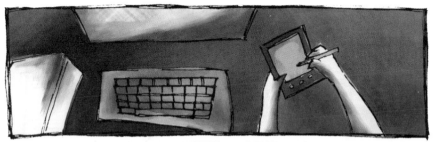

34

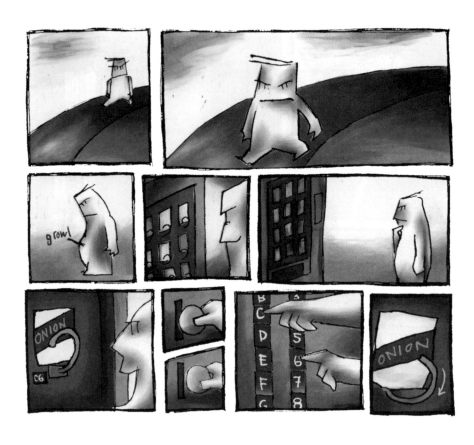

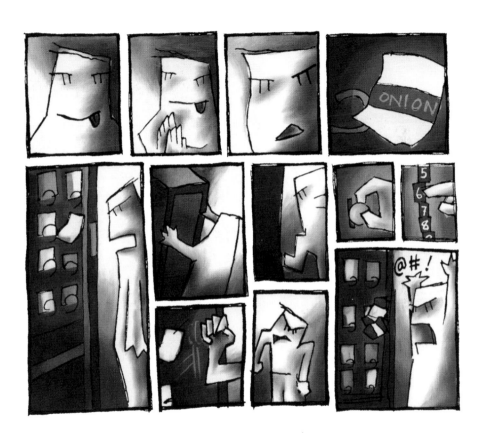

chapter 2

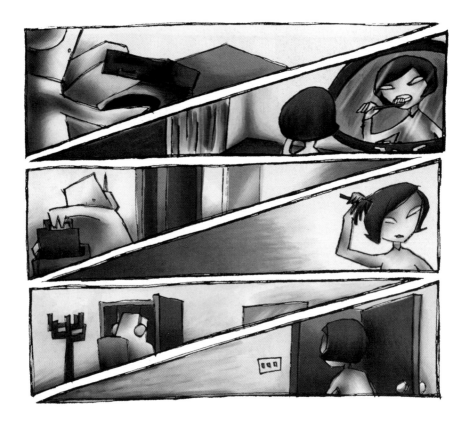

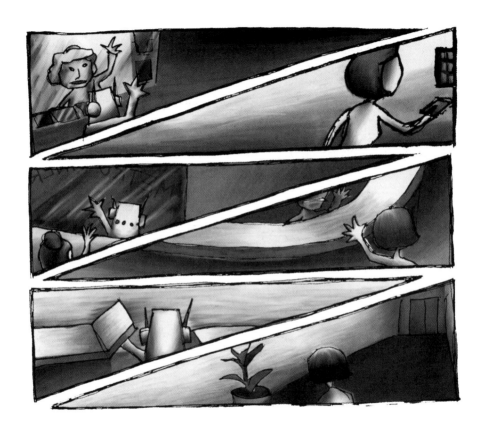

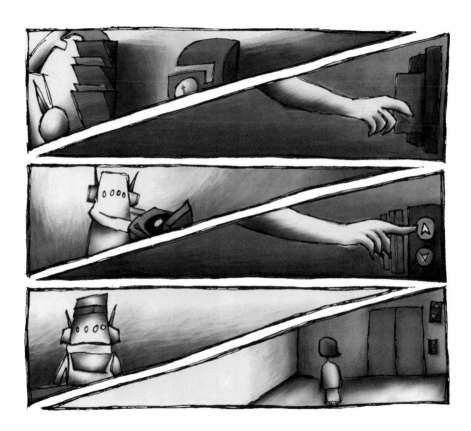

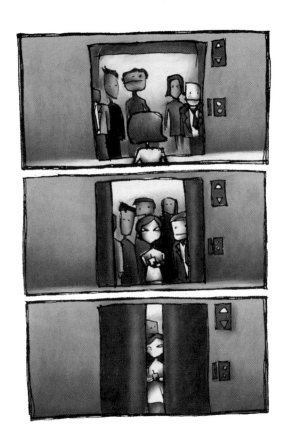

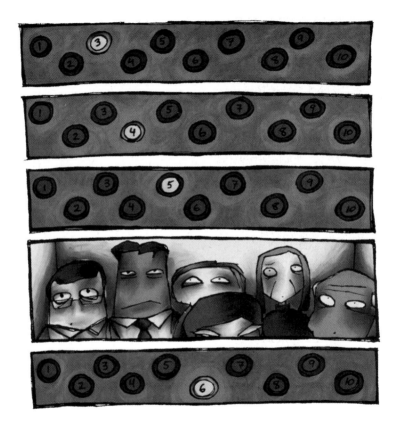

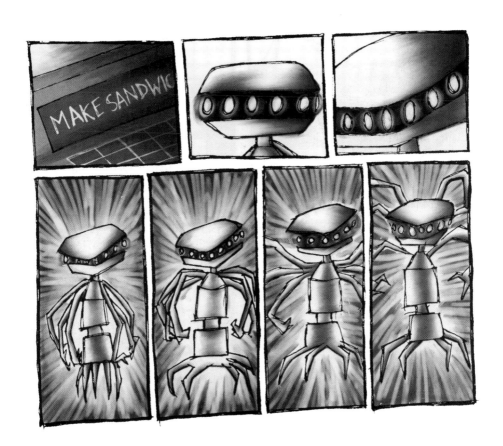

chapter 3

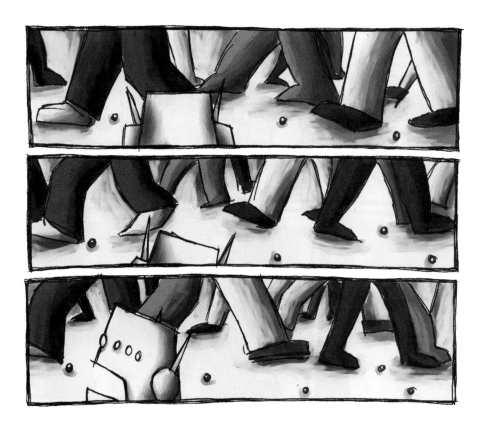

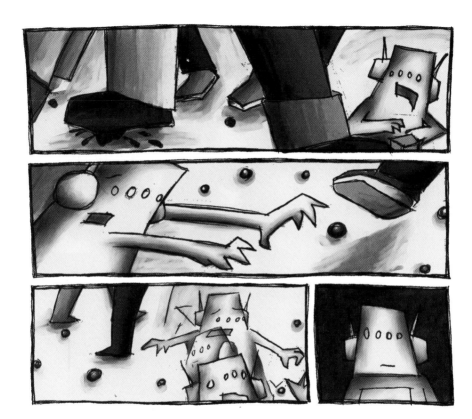

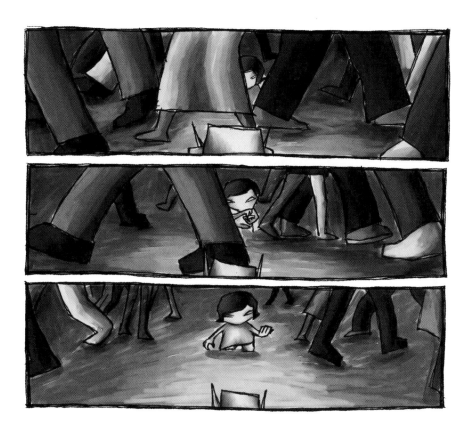

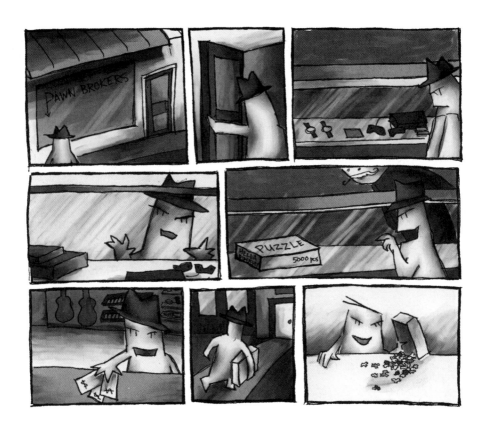

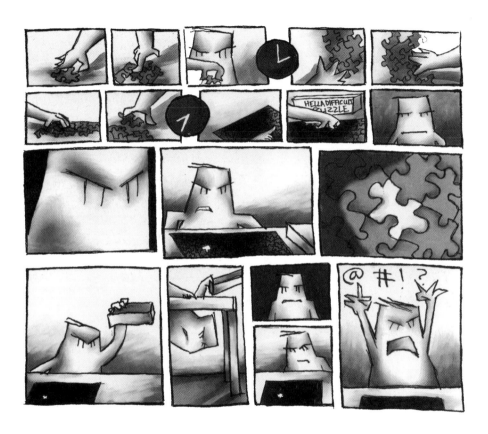

chapter 4

EXCITING NEW
SUBMIT CD OF
SONG TO LOVE SONG
NO LATER THAN APRIL
CLOSE A CHEQUE FOR $40
CESSING FEE MADE
GIBLE FOR
PUBLIC LIBRARY
LOVE SONGS FOR IDIOTS

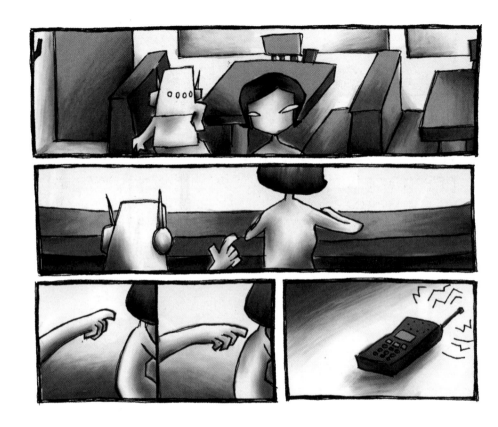

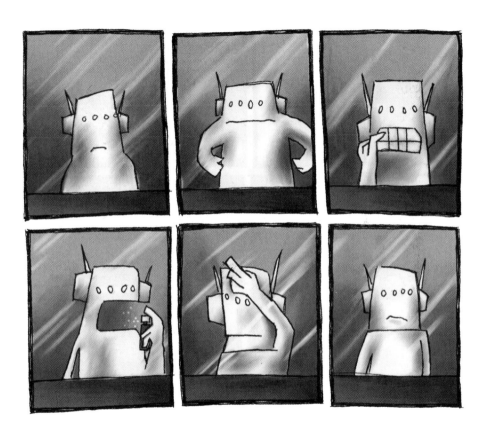

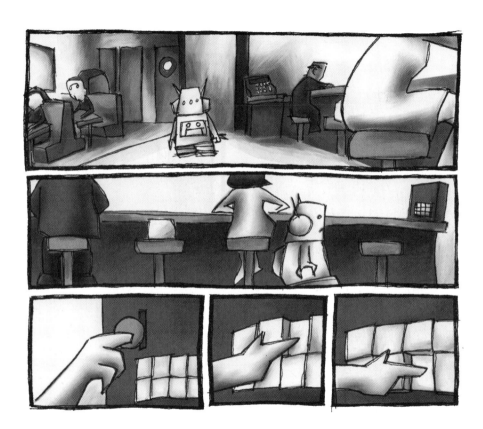

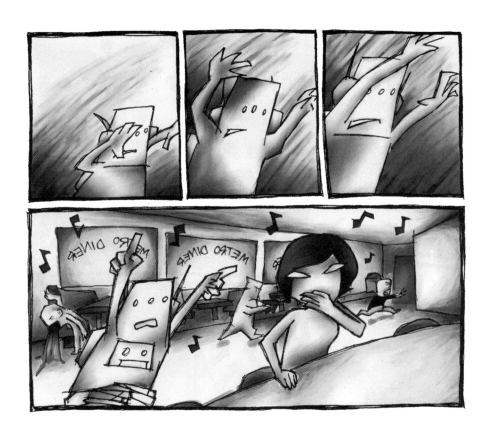

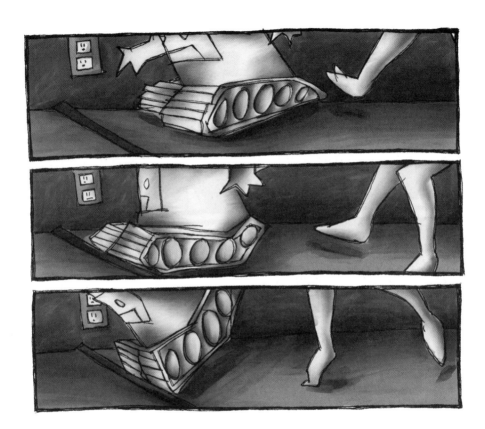

chapter 5

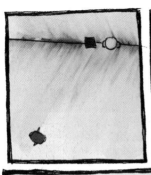

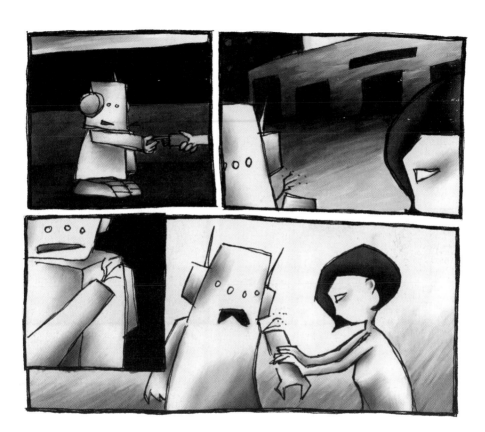

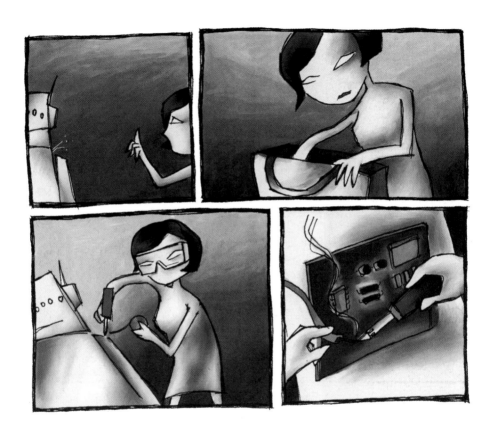

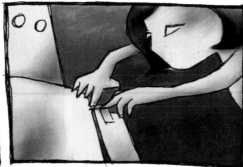

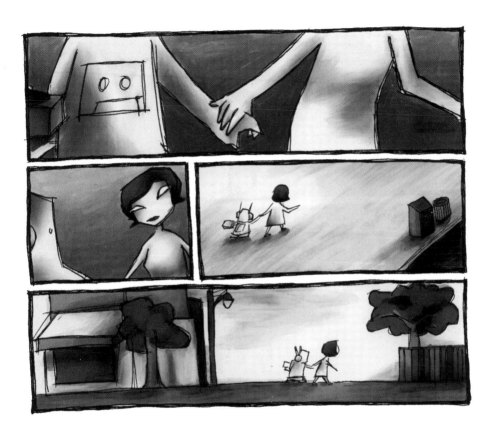

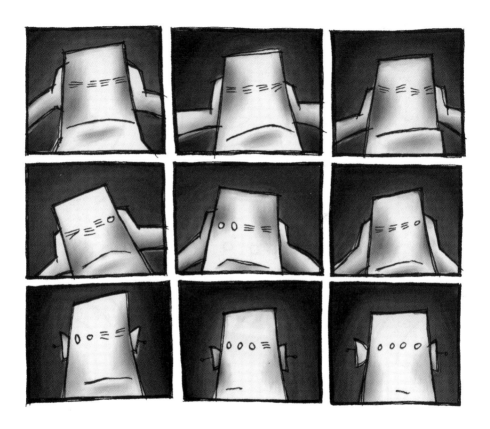

chapter 6

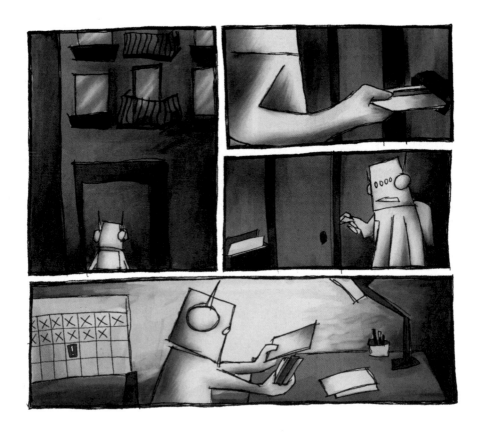

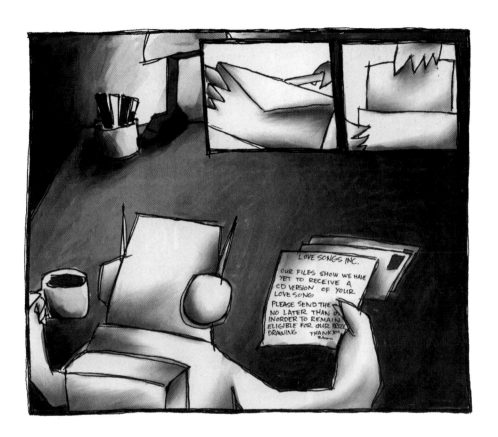

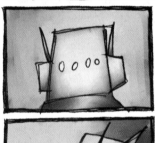

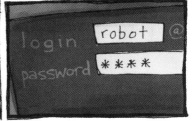

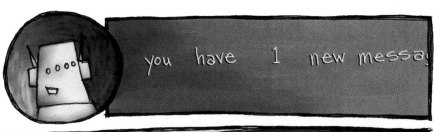

you   have   1   new messag

from: malorie@nufonia.com

dinner tomorrow night at my apartm

44   Mentana St.
Z city
3rd buzzer

hope you can make it, it's my birthday.
xx malorie

chapter 7

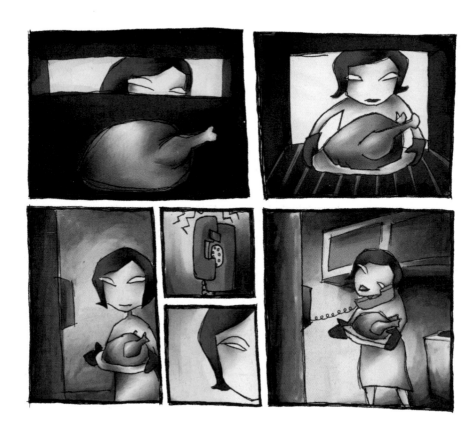

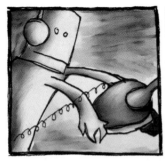

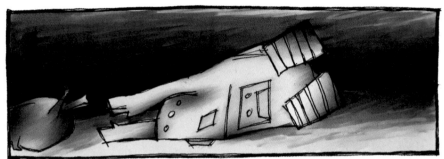

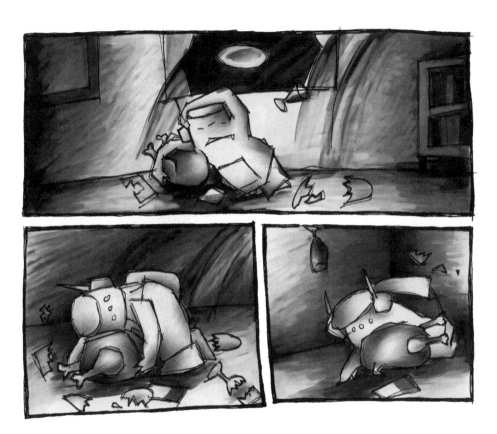

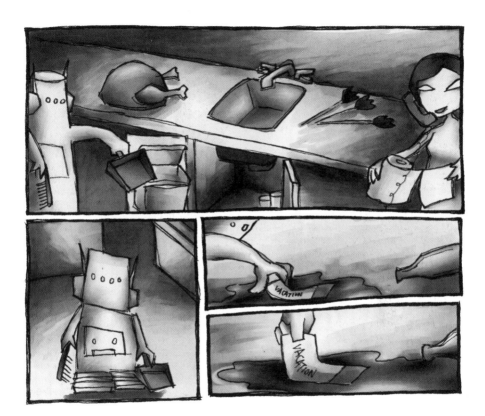

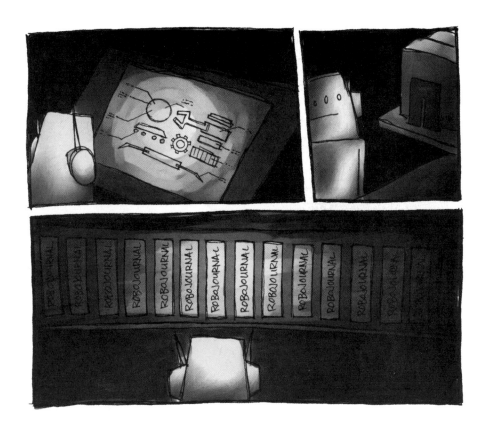

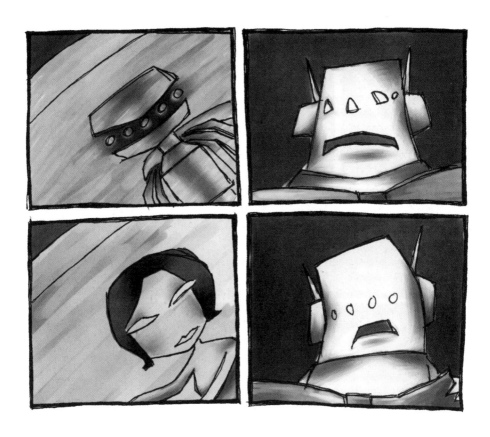

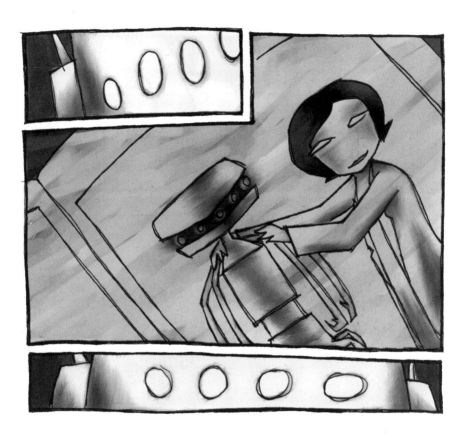

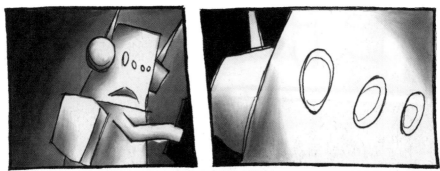

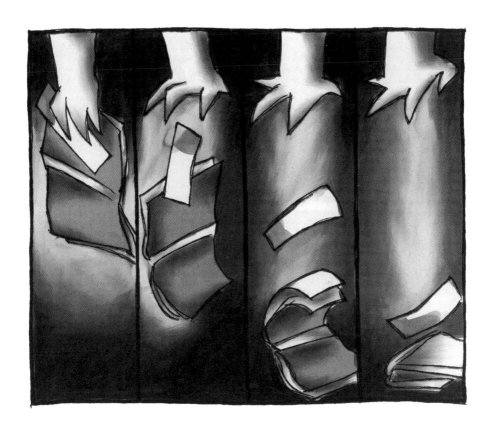

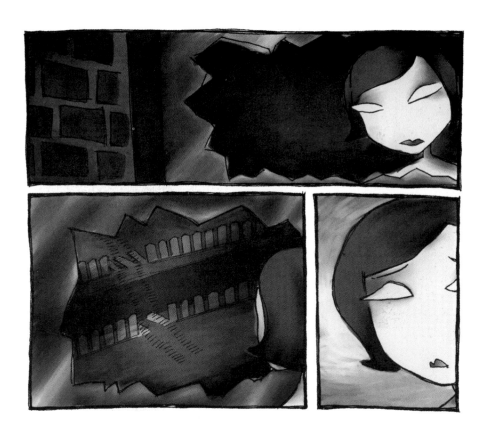

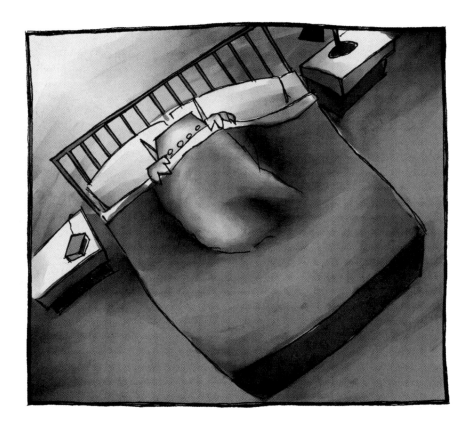

chapter 8

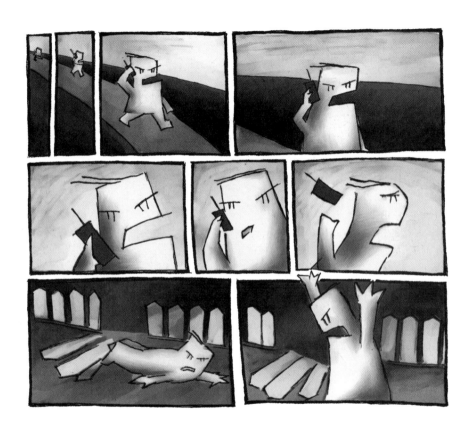

249

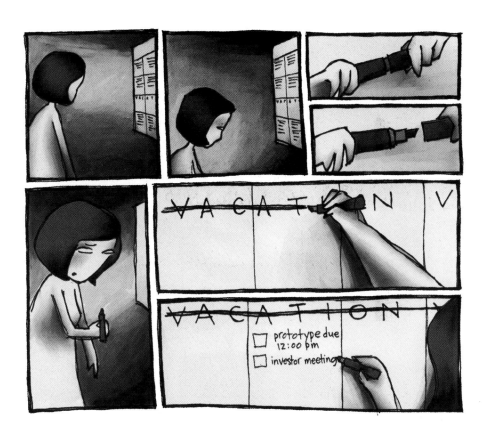

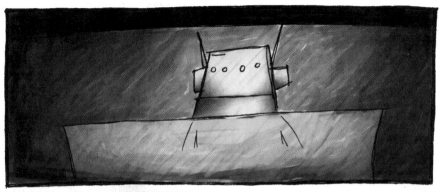

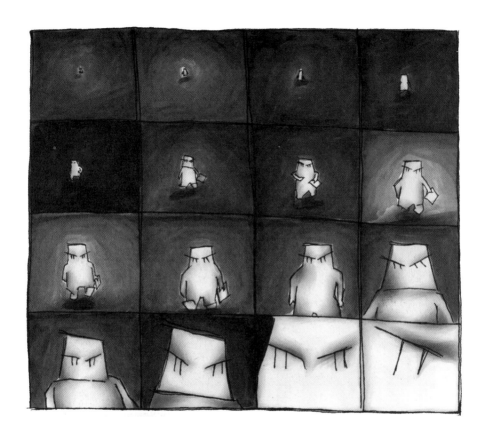

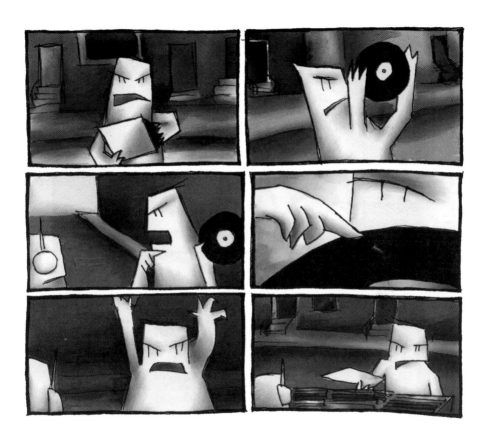

music for
rollerska[

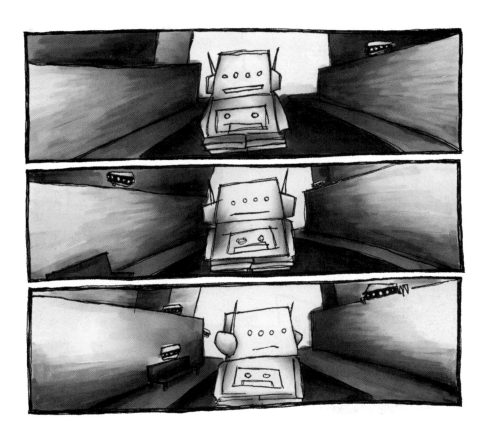

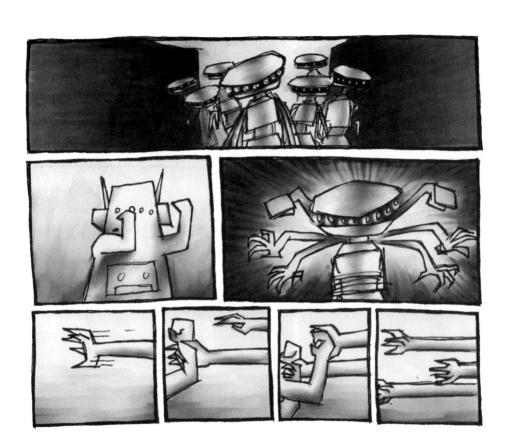

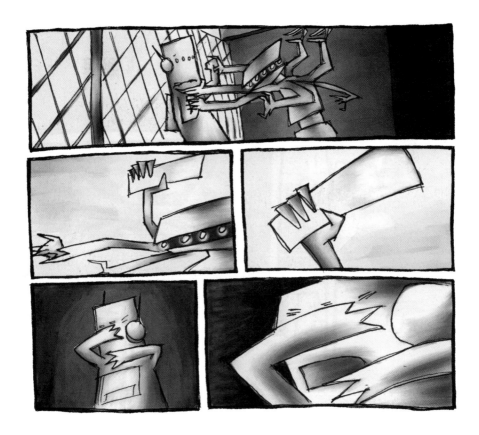

VACATION
ISLAND
AIR

WELCOMES
✳ INDUSTRIES
EMPLOYEES
& GUESTS

305

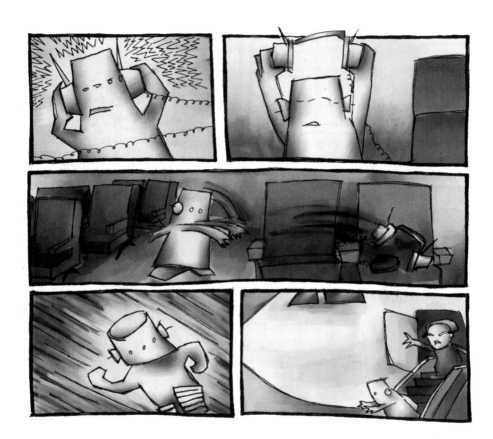

editor: emma mckay
cover design: eric san & louisa schabas
original layout: louisa schabas
travel edition layout: pat hamou
production: emma mckay

all tracks written and produced by kid koala
except "epilogue" written and produced by kid koala and vid cousins
piano and turntables: kid koala
violins, violas, cellos: afiara quartet
string arrangements on "epilogue": vid cousins
mastered at studio victor by fernand martell and assisted by carl bastien
"epilogue" mixed and mastered at monkey puzzle sound studios by vid cousins
music published by just isn't music ltd.
kid koala appears courtesy of ninja tune

management
ryhna thompson / envision management
www.envisionmanagement.com